Sam and Lizzie went to
Dad's garage.

Rosie was at the car wash.

Car
Wash

Lizzie said, 'I want a go.'

FRESH
PEUGEOT
205 GTI
K727 GGJ

Lizzie got into the car.
Sam got in too.

The car went into the car wash.

The brushes came down.
The water came down.

Lizzie didn't like the car wash.
She cried.

She shouted, ‘I want to get out!
I want to get out!’

Then she hid on the floor.

The car wash stopped.

Sam and Rosie got out.

But Lizzie didn't want to get out.

She shouted, ‘I want another go!’